WE Make Up The World

Written By: Janelle Oliveira

Illustrations By: Julios Ruden D. Francisco

ISBN: **9798448046926**

Konnichiwa, I say hello to you. My name is Akari. How do you do?

I live in Japan with my family. There's my Haha, my Chichi, and of course there is me.

We gather around the table for dinner time. Soba, delicious, it's a favorite of mine.

See I am similar to you over there. I have a nose, two eyes, and straight black hair.

I laugh, play games, and enjoy my day.
I am from Japan and this is our way.

*Konnichiwa (Kon-nee-chee-wah) *Haha-Mother *Chichi-Father
*Soba-Thin Japanese noodles

JAPAN

Ola, I say hello to you. My name is Pedro. How do you do?

I live in Portugal with my family. There's my Mãe, my Pai, and of course there is me.

We gather around the table for dinner time. Bacalhau, delicious, it's a favorite of mine.

See I am similar to you over there. I have a nose, two eyes, and wavy brown hair.

I laugh, play games, and enjoy my day.
I am from Portugal and this is our way.

*Ola (O-l'a) *Mae-Mother *Pai-Father *Bacalhau (buh-kal-hua) - Cod fish dinner

PORTUGAL

Guten Tag, I say hello to you. My name is Johanna. How do you do?

I live in Germany with my family. There's my Mutter, my Vater, and of course there is me.

We gather around the table for dinner time. Sauerbraten, delicious, it's a favorite of mine.

See I am similar to you over there. I have a nose, two eyes, and sunny blonde hair.

I laugh, play games, and enjoy my day.
I am from Germany and this is our way.

*Mutter-Mother *Vater-Father *Sauerbraten-A pickled/ vinegar Roast

GERMANY

As-Salam-u-Alaikum, I say hello to you. My name is Ahmed. How do you do?

I live in Pakistan with my family. There's my Ammi, my Abbu, and of course there is me.

We gather around the table for dinner time. Haleem, delicious, it's a favorite of mine.

See I am similar to you over there. I have a nose, two eyes, and the darkest brown hair.

I laugh, play games, and enjoy my day.
I am from Pakistan and this is our way.

*As-Salam-u-Alaikum (us-saa-laam-muu-alie-kum) *Ammi-Mother *Abbu-Father *Haleem-Popular Stew made up of wheat and barley

PAKISTAN

Bonjour, I say hello to you. My name is Brigitte. How do you do?

I live in France with my family. There's my Mère, my Père, and of course there is me.

We gather around the table for dinner time. Bouillabaisse, delicious, it's a favorite of mine.

See I am similar to you over there. I have a nose, two eyes, and ginger red hair.

I laugh, play games, and enjoy my day.
I am from France and this is our way.

*Bonjour-(bon-jour) *Mère-Mother,*Père-Father *Bouillabaisse-Traditional Fish Stew

FRANCE

Sannu, I say hello to you. My name is Halimah. How do you do?

I live in Nigeria with my family. There's my Uwa, my Uba, and of course there is me.

We gather around the table for dinner time. Dambu Nama delicious, it's a favorite of mine.

See I am similar to you over there. I have a nose, two eyes, and braided black hair.

I laugh, play games, and enjoy my day.
I am from Nigeria and this is our way.

*Uwa-Mother,*Uba-Father *Dambu Nama-Fried & shredded meat dish

NiGERiA

Hola, I say hello to you. My name is Javier. How do you do?

I live in Mexico with my family. There's my Madre, my Padre, and of course there is me.

We gather around the table for dinner time. Tostada delicious, it's a favorite of mine.

See I am similar to you over there. I have a nose, two eyes, and thick dark hair.

I laugh, play games, and enjoy my day.
I am from Mexico and this is our way.

Madre-Mother, Padre-Father *Tostada-Deep fried tortilla base with toppings

MEXICO

Yassas, I say hello to you. My name is Nico. How do you do?

I live in Greece with my family. There's my Mitéra, my Patéras, and of course there is me.

We gather around the table for dinner time. Moussaka, delicious, it's a favorite of mine.

See I am similar to you over there. I have a nose, two eyes, and light brown hair.

I laugh, play games, and enjoy my day.
I am from Greece and this is our way.

*Yassas (Yah-sas) *Mitéra-Mother,*Patéras-Father *Moussaka- A layered casserole dish with meat, potatoes, eggplant

GREECE

Oi, I say hello to you. My name is Juliana. How do you do?

I live in Brazil with my family. There's my Mamãe, my Paizinho, and of course there is me.

We gather around the table for dinner time. Feijoada delicious, it's a favorite of mine.

See I am similar to you over there. I have a nose, two eyes, and curly brown hair.

I laugh, play games, and enjoy my day.
I am from Brazil and this is our way.

*Mamãe-Mother,*Paizinho-Father(Pai-zi-nho) *Feijoada (fay-jow-aa-duh)-Pork, beef & bean stew

BRAZIL

Kamusta I say hello to you. My name is Amado. How do you do?

I live in The Philippines with my family. There's my Nanay, my Tatay, and of course there is me.

We gather around the table for dinner time. Sinigang, delicious, it's a favorite of mine.

See I am similar to you over there. I have a nose, two eyes, and wispy black hair.

I laugh, play games, and enjoy my day.
I am from The Philippines and this is our way.

*Kamusta (Ku-mus-ta) *Nanay-Mother,*Tatay-Father *Sinigang- A very popular sour and savory soup

PHILIPPINES

Hi, I say hello to you. My name is Christopher. How do you do?

I live in The United States of America with my family. There's my Mother, my Father, and of course there is me.

We gather around the table for dinner time. Meatloaf, delicious, it's a favorite of mine.

See I am similar to you over there. I have a nose, two eyes, and dark blonde hair.

I laugh, play games, and enjoy my day.
I am from The U.S.A. and this is our way.

*Meatloaf-ground meat & seasonings baked in the shape of a loaf

UNITED STATES OF AMERICA

Our language, our country, together we'll share.

Teaching differences amongst us, with much love and care.

Shades of colors, and cultures, our world was built.

Together we're woven like a beautiful quilt.

About the Author

Janelle Oliveira has a deep passion for writing, as well as teaching and sharing kindness with her words. She wants to shape young minds and engage them in fun-filled stories, while teaching them life lessons along the way. She currently has a few other children books she is busy working on as well as 3 previous published titles. Mommy's Heart, A World Of Animal Friends, & Count My love, are her three other titles available for sale on Amazon.com, as well as her Bookshop on Bookbaby,com. Be on the lookout for her many more books to come. Janelle loves being able to bring joy, kindness, and love into your home and into the hands of early readers.

Made in the USA
Middletown, DE
29 April 2022